Excellence
in Word
Problems

Year 5

By Richard Cooper

RISING★STARS

Rising Stars UK Ltd., 76 Farnaby Road, Bromley,
BR1 4BH

Website: **www.risingstars-uk.com**

Every effort has been made to trace copyright
holders and obtain their permission for the use
of copyright material. The authors and
publishers will gladly receive information
enabling them to rectify any error or omission in
subsequent editions.

All facts are correct at time of going to press.

Published 2003
Text, design and layout ©Rising Stars UK Ltd.
Editorial: Tanya Solomons
Concept design: Burville Riley
Design: Ken Vail Graphic Design, Cambridge
Illustration copyright ©Louisa Burville-Riley
Cover photo ©Mark Scott/Getty Images

British Library Cataloguing in Publication Data

A CIP record for this book is available from the
British Library.

ISBN 1-904591-21-3

Printed by Wyndeham Gait.

Contents

How to use this book

The *Excellence in Word Problems* series is designed to help you use your mathematical skills to solve a range a problems, many of which are written in words rather than figures.

Rather than giving a sum like:

$4 \times 6 =$ ☐

a word problem might be along the lines of:

"If I have 4 six packs of cola, how many cans of cola do I have in total?"

The answer is the same, but you need to think about it a bit more and remember to answer by writing or saying: **"I have 24 cans of cola in total."**

The introduction

This section of each page gives you an idea of the sort of problems you are likely to see and helps you to understand what maths you need to use.

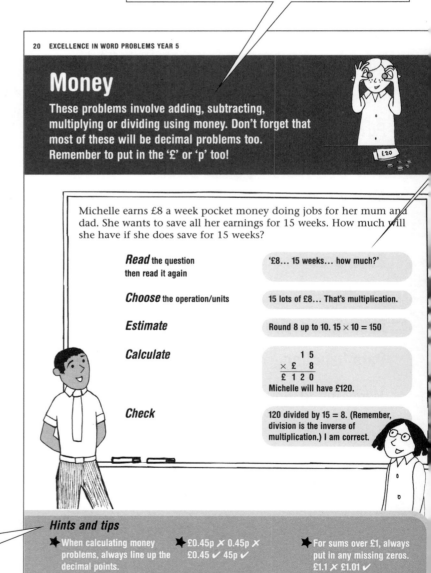

20   EXCELLENCE IN WORD PROBLEMS YEAR 5

Money

These problems involve adding, subtracting, multiplying or dividing using money. Don't forget that most of these will be decimal problems too. Remember to put in the '£' or 'p' too!

Michelle earns £8 a week pocket money doing jobs for her mum and dad. She wants to save all her earnings for 15 weeks. How much will she have if she does save for 15 weeks?

Read the question then read it again	'£8... 15 weeks... how much?'
Choose the operation/units	15 lots of £8... That's multiplication.
Estimate	Round 8 up to 10. 15 × 10 = 150
Calculate	1 5 × £ 8 £ 1 2 0 Michelle will have £120.
Check	120 divided by 15 = 8. (Remember, division is the inverse of multiplication.) I am correct.

Hints and tips

★ When calculating money problems, always line up the decimal points.

★ £0.45p ✗ 0.45p ✗ £0.45 ✔ 45p ✔

★ For sums over £1, always put in any missing zeros. £1.1 ✗ £1.01 ✔

Hints and tips

The hints and tips section gives you useful ideas for completing the problems on the other page. These are the things you need to remember if you are doing a quiz or test!

The example problem

The flow chart takes you through an example problem *step-by-step*. This is important when answering word problems as it helps you to order your thoughts, do each part of the problem in the right order and *check your work*!

Every problem has the same five steps.
READ the question then read it again
CHOOSE your operations and units
ESTIMATE your answer
CALCULATE
CHECK your answer

We remember this by using this mnemonic:
RED
CLOWNS
ENTER
CAVES
CAREFULLY

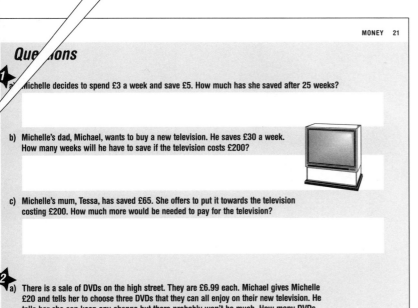

MONEY   21

Questions

1

a) Michelle decides to spend £3 a week and save £5. How much has she saved after 25 weeks?

b) Michelle's dad, Michael, wants to buy a new television. He saves £30 a week. How many weeks will he have to save if the television costs £200?

c) Michelle's mum, Tessa, has saved £65. She offers to put it towards the television costing £200. How much more would be needed to pay for the television?

2

a) There is a sale of DVDs on the high street. They are £6.99 each. Michael gives Michelle £20 and tells her to choose three DVDs that they can all enjoy on their new television. He tells her she can keep any change but there probably won't be much. How many DVDs does Michelle buy and how much change can she keep?

b) Tessa decided to rent her favourite film – Spiderman 2. It costs £2.50 a night with a £20 fine if the film is damaged. She kept the film for 6 nights. Unfortunately, it had also been left on top of the radiator – it was ruined! How much did Tessa have to pay altogether?

Challenge

Which is the greater amount – three of every note and coin here or £1 a day for a year? What is the difference in totals?

£50   £20   £10   £5

The questions

The questions get harder as you go down the page.

- Section 1 questions are fairly straightforward and help you to practise your skills.
- Section 2 questions are a bit harder but will help you to remember all the key points.
- The Challenge sections are really tough and sometimes mean that you can make up games and your own questions! They can be great fun!

All about word problems

Ten top tips for working with word problems

1 *Work step-by-step.* Follow the flow chart.

Red   **R**ead the question then read it again
Clowns   **C**hoose your operations and units
Enter   **E**stimate your answer
Caves   **C**alculate
Carefully   **C**heck your answer

2 Always *show your working* or 'method'. This will help you to keep track of what you have done and may help you to get extra marks.

3 Always *include your units* in the answer. If you don't, you won't get full marks.

4 When you first read through a question, *underline important words and numbers*. This will help you to remember the important bits!

5 *Draw a picture* to help you. Sometimes a question is easier if you can 'see' it. Drawing 6 apples can help you if you need to divide them!

6 If the problem has a number of steps, break it down and do *one step at a time*.

7 When *checking your answers*, look at the inverse operation.

8 Sometimes an answer will 'sound right'. Read it out (quietly) and listen. *Does it make sense?*

9 If you are using measurements (grams, litres, cm), make sure that the *units are the same* before you calculate.

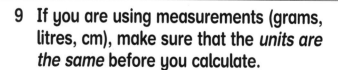

10 Once again! *Read the question then read it again.*

Place value

Place value questions will often ask you to make up a large or small number using different digits. Remember, each digit has a different value depending on where you put it.

Mehmet has five digit cards. They are: six, three, eight, nine and four. He can only use each card once. What is the largest 3-digit number he can make? Write your answer in words.

Read the question then read it again	'Write your answer in words…'
Choose the operation/units	I'm ordering the digits, largest one first.
Estimate	The number will be nine hundred and something.
Calculate	9 then 8 then 6. Nine hundred and eighty-six is the largest number Mehmet can make.
Check	Yes, the number is the largest and it's spelt correctly.

Hints and tips

★ The further LEFT of the decimal point, the LARGER the value of the digit.

★ 2000.00
The '2' has a value of two thousand.

★ 20.00
The '2' has a value of twenty.

Questions

a) What is the smallest 3-digit number Mehmet can make with his cards? Write your answer in words.

b) What is the second largest 3-digit number Mehmet can make with his cards? Write your answer in words.

c) What is the second smallest 3-digit number Mehmet can make with his cards? Write your answer in words.

a) Mehmet swaps all five of his cards for five different digit cards. What is the largest 3-digit number he can make if he only uses each new card once? Write your answer in words.

b) What is the smallest 3-digit number Mehmet can make if he is allowed to use all of the digit cards any number of times?

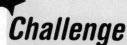

Challenge

Can you help Mehmet write these large numbers in figures?

Three hundred and ninety-six thousand, four hundred and seventy-one.

One million, nineteen thousand and thirteen.

Forty-nine million, seventy-three thousand and one.

Fractions

Fraction problems are tricky. You might be asked to find a fraction of a number, e.g. 'What is half of 30?' You may also be asked to work out 'What fraction of 30 is 15?'

Wesley's dad spends 8 hours per day at work as a mechanic, 6 hours at home awake and 10 hours per day in bed asleep. What fraction of the day does Wesley's dad spend at work?

Read the question then read it again	*'What fraction... at work...'*
Choose the operation/units	8 hours *out of* 24... that's division!
Estimate	12 hours is half of 24 so less than a half.
Calculate	$\frac{8}{24} = \frac{1}{3}$ Wesley's dad spends $\frac{1}{3}$ of the day at work.
Check	Yes, $\frac{1}{3}$ of 24 is the same as dividing 24 by 3... ...which is 8. I was correct!

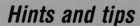

Hints and tips

★ Finding $\frac{1}{2}$ of something is the same as dividing it by 2.

★ Finding $\frac{1}{3}$ of something is the same as dividing it by 3.
Finding $\frac{1}{4}$ of something is the same as dividing it by 4.

Questions

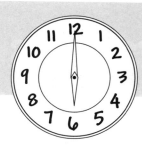

a) What fraction of the day does Wesley's dad spend at home awake?

b) Wesley's mum has a part time job for three hours a day making jewellery.
What fraction of the day does she spend at work?

c) What fraction of the day does Wesley spend on his homework if it takes him two hours each evening?

a) There are 50 pupils in Wesley's year group at school. Three tenths of them don't like PE lessons. The rest do. How many pupils in Wesley's year like PE lessons?

b) Wesley lives 1 kilometre from his school. He rides his scooter for $\frac{9}{10}$ of the way and walks the rest of the distance. How far does Wesley walk to school each day?

Challenge

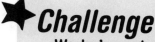

Wesley's great granny sent him a puzzle in a card for his ninth birthday. If Wesley could solve it, she promised not to give him a big sloppy kiss in front of his friends at his party! The puzzle was…
'You have been alive for $\frac{1}{9}$ of my life. How old am I?'
Wesley answered '72'. Did Wesley get a sloppy kiss? Explain your answer.

Decimals

Decimal problems can be about distance or time. Don't forget to add the units! These questions use addition and subtraction but watch out for the Challenge!

At the school sports day, Phoebe came second in the long jump with a leap of 2.8 m. Marie jumped 35 cm further and won. How far in metres did Marie jump?

Read the question then read it again	'2.8 m... 35 cm... how far?'
Choose the operation/units	Addition and metres.
Estimate	The answer will be more than 3 metres but it must be realistic.
Calculate	2.8 m = 280 cm 280 cm + 35 cm = 315 cm Answer in metres, so 315 cm = 3.15 m. Marie jumped 3.15 m.
Check	315 cm − 35 cm = 280 cm. I'm correct.

Hints and tips

★ When dealing with mixed decimals such as 2.8 and 1.54, add any missing zeros to make ordering or calculating much easier.
e.g. 2.8 + 1.54 becomes 2.80 + 1.54

★ Picture the decimal on a number line: 5 is halfway along, 0.75 is three quarters of the way along and 0.25 is one quarter of the way along the line.

Questions

1

a) Phoebe threw the javelin 11.5 m. This was 60 cm further than Marie. How far in metres did Marie throw the javelin?

b) Marie ran the 100 m in 16.7 seconds. Phoebe was 1 second faster. What was Phoebe's time for the 100 m?

c) Marie cleared 1.21 m in the high jump. Phoebe jumped 30 cm less. How high in metres did Phoebe jump?

2

a) Theo, Larissa and Sasha ran in the 200 m. Sasha was 4.5 seconds quicker than Theo but 2.7 seconds behind Larissa. Theo completed the race in 32.1 seconds. What was Larissa's time in seconds?

b) Theo, Larissa and Sasha also ran in the school cross-country race. This time Theo was 4 minutes faster than Larissa who finished in 25.5 minutes. Sasha was 10 minutes slower than Larissa. How much faster was Theo than Sasha?

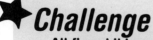**Challenge**

All five children formed a tug of war team. This is how much each of them weighed:
Theo 48.8 kg, Sasha 37.2 kg, Marie 45.5 kg, Phoebe 42.4 kg, Larissa 44.8 kg
They won three matches in a row before losing in the final to a team that was 5000 g lighter than them. How heavy were the winning team? Give your answer in kg.

Percentages

Percentage problems are usually about money.
Some questions ask for a percentage of an amount of money, e.g. 10% of £1. Other questions might ask you to work out 10% off a price.

Lee wants to buy a new pair of trainers. A pair of 'Reeburks' are priced at £40 but are on special offer with 20% off the price. How much would Lee pay for the trainers now?

Read the question then read it again

'£40... 20% off... how much?'

Choose the operation/units

Percent means 'out of a hundred'. The units are £.

Estimate

20% is the same as a fifth...

Calculate

10% of 40 = 4 so 20% = 8
£40 − £8 = £32
Lee would pay £32 for the trainers.

Hints and tips

★ Learn these percentage/ decimal/fraction equivalents (equivalent means 'the same').

$1\% = 0.01 = \frac{1}{100}$

$10\% = 0.1 = \frac{1}{10}$

$20\% = 0.2 = \frac{1}{5}$

$25\% = 0.25 = \frac{1}{4}$

$50\% = 0.5 = \frac{1}{2}$

$75\% = 0.75 = \frac{3}{4}$

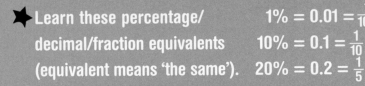

Questions

a) Lee's mum Debbie goes to the same shop. She sees a tracksuit priced at £30. The sales assistant says she can have the tracksuit with a 30% discount because it's slightly damaged. How much would Debbie have to pay?

b) Lee's sister Faye wants to have tennis lessons. The normal price is £20 per hour but during Wimbledon there is an amazing 50% off! How much is a tennis lesson during Wimbledon?

c) Lee joins the local athletics club. The cost of membership is £100 per year with 75% off for under 16s. Lee is 10. How much does he pay to join for a year?

2

a) Faye needs a new tennis racket. She sees one in the sports shop priced £50 and the same racket in the department store for £80 with a 50% discount in the summer sale. Which one should she buy? What is the difference in price?

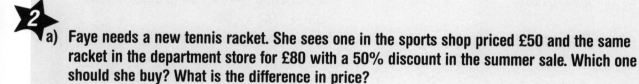

b) Debbie starts going to aerobics classes. They cost £5 a class but if you book a course of 12 you get a 20% discount. How much does Debbie pay for a course of 12?

Challenge

Debbie, Lee and Faye have £1000 saved in the bank. Debbie takes out 50%, Lee takes 10% and Faye takes 15% to spend on holiday. They each come home with 10% of their spending money left. How much does each of them have when they get home?

Addition

Most of these addition problems ask you to add two 3-digit numbers. That can be tricky. Remember to line up the numbers accurately in the sum – then you will be fine.

Lewis and Derelle collect football stickers. Lewis has 418 and Derelle has 196. How many do they have altogether?

Read the question then read it again

'418… 196… altogether…'

Choose the operation/units

Altogether means 'add'.

Estimate

418 is close to 400, 196 is close to 200.
400 + 200 = 600

Calculate

```
    4 1 8
  + 1 9 6
    6 1 4
```
Lewis and Derelle have 614 stickers.

Check

I'll check using the inverse method.
614 − 418 = 196.
Also, 614 is very close to my estimate.

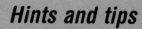

Hints and tips

★ 'increase by' 'how many altogether' 'add'
'what is the total of…' 'find the sum of…'
All these terms and phrases mean ADDITION.

Questions

a) Richard has 244 stickers and Danny gives him 65 of his 'swaps'. How many stickers does Richard have in total?

b) Danny has 186 stickers. He increases his collection by 48. How many stickers does he have now?

c) Anna and Sita start collecting. Anna has 163 stickers and Sita has 152. What is the sum of Anna and Sita's collection?

a) To complete the collection you need to have 526 stickers. Lewis has 418 and Derelle has 196. How many does each of them need to complete their collections?

b) Anna has 163 stickers but Sita gets bored of collecting and gives her 152 stickers to Anna. Anna has got 78 of them already! How many stickers does Anna now need to complete the collection of 526?

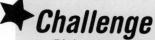 Challenge

Richard sets Danny a challenge. Richard shows Danny a grid of nine squares (3 × 3). Danny must place a sticker on the first square then double the number of stickers on each square until he has filled the grid. How many stickers would there be on the ninth square?
What if the grid was 4 × 4? How many stickers would there be on the sixteenth square?

Subtraction

These subtraction problems are taking away a 2-digit number from a 3-digit number. Estimating first will help you get these right.

Hannah and Lucy have written their names using shells in sand on the beach. Hannah used 82 shells; Lucy used 29 less than Hannah. How many shells did Lucy use?

Read the question then read it again

'82... 29... less than...'

Choose the operation/units

'Less than' means subtract.

Estimate

Rounding method... 80 – 30 = 50

Calculate

82 – 29 = 53
Lucy used 53 shells.

Check

53 + 29 = 82
Also, 53 is close to my estimate.

Hints and tips

★ 'less than' 'difference' 'decrease' 'subtract'. All these terms and phrases mean SUBTRACTION.

★ Picture the numbers in your head when you estimate.

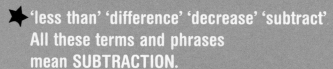

Questions

1

a) Jonathan and Joe wrote their names using pebbles. Jonathan used 258 pebbles and Joe used 89. How many more pebbles did Jonathan use than Joe?

b) Jonathan counted 47 seagulls on the cliff-top. When he counted the number of seagulls by the harbour there were 130. What was the difference between the number of seagulls on the cliff-top and the number of seagulls by the harbour?

c) Joe decorated his sandcastle with 162 shells. Hannah took 65 shells away to put on her sandcastle! How many shells did Joe have left?

2

a) Lucy bought herself, Joe, Hannah and Jonathan ice creams costing 80p each. How much change did she get from a £10 note?

b) Lucy, Hannah, Jonathan and Joe had a game of beach cricket. The girls scored 172 runs. The boys scored 17 less. Joe scored 56 runs. How many did Jonathan score?

⭐ Challenge

Here are some famous dates in history.

1969 – Neil Armstrong walks on the Moon.

1903 – The Wright brothers fly the first manned flight.

1837 – Victoria is crowned queen.

1605 – Guy Fawkes and the gunpowder plot.

1485 – Columbus sails to America.

1066 – The Battle of Hastings.

Write down the current year. (2003, 2004 etc.)

Can you work out how many years ago these events took place?

Money

These problems involve adding, subtracting, multiplying or dividing using money. Don't forget that most of these will be decimal problems too. Remember to put in the '£' or 'p' too!

Michelle earns £8 a week pocket money doing jobs for her mum and dad. She wants to save all her earnings for 15 weeks. How much will she have if she does save for 15 weeks?

Read the question then read it again	'£8... 15 weeks... how much?'
Choose the operation/units	15 lots of £8... That's multiplication.
Estimate	Round 8 up to 10. $15 \times 10 = 150$
Calculate	$$\begin{array}{r} 1\ 5 \\ \times\ £\quad 8 \\ \hline £\ 1\ 2\ 0 \end{array}$$ Michelle will have £120.
Check	120 divided by 15 = 8. (Remember, division is the inverse of multiplication.) I am correct.

Hints and tips

★ When calculating money problems, always line up the decimal points.

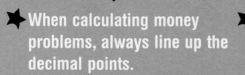

★ £0.45p ✗ 0.45p ✗ £0.45 ✔ 45p ✔

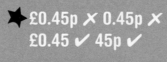

★ For sums over £1, always put in any missing zeros. £1.1 ✗ £1.01 ✔

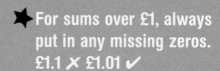

Questions

1

a) Michelle decides to spend £3 a week and save £5. How much has she saved after 25 weeks?

b) Michelle's dad, Michael, wants to buy a new television. He saves £30 a week. How many weeks will he have to save if the television costs £200?

c) Michelle's mum, Tessa, has saved £65. She offers to put it towards the television costing £200. How much more would be needed to pay for the television?

2

a) There is a sale of DVDs on the high street. They are £6.99 each. Michael gives Michelle £20 and tells her to choose three DVDs that they can all enjoy on their new television. He tells her she can keep any change but there probably won't be much. How many DVDs does Michelle buy and how much change can she keep?

b) Tessa decided to rent her favourite film – Spiderman 2. It costs £2.50 a night with a £20 fine if the film is damaged. She kept the film for 6 nights. Unfortunately, it had also been left on top of the radiator – it was ruined! How much did Tessa have to pay altogether?

★Challenge

| £50 | £20 | £10 | £5 |

Which is the greater amount – three of every note and coin here or £1 a day for a year?
What is the difference in totals?

Time

Time problems can ask you to work out how many minutes there are between two times. They can also ask you to work out what time is 30 minutes later than, say, 13:00. Remember the 24 hour clock!

Lihan and his friends are visiting 'Chunder Towers' amusement park for a birthday treat. They arrive at 09:45 and plan to stay for $6\frac{1}{2}$ hours. At what time will they leave the park?

Read the question then read it again

'09:45… $6\frac{1}{2}$… at what time?'

Choose the operation/units

Counting on. It's addition… hours and minutes.

Estimate

$9 + 6 = 15$… 15:00?

Calculate

$09:45 + 6 = 15:45$
$15:45 + \frac{1}{2}(30 \text{ mins.}) = 16:15$
They will leave the park at 16:15.

Check

$16:15 - 06:30 = 09:45$

Hints and tips

★ 1 millennium = 1000 years
★ 1 century = 100 years
★ 1 decade = 10 years
★ 1 year = 12 months or 52 weeks or 365 days

★ 1 leap year = 366 days ('Olympic years' are leap years: 2004, 2000, 1996, 1992 etc.)
★ 1 week = 7 days
★ 1 day = 24 hours
★ 1 hour = 60 minutes
★ 1 minute = 60 seconds

Questions

a) Lihan queues up to go on the 'Avenger' rollercoaster. He starts queuing at 10:05 and gets on the ride at 10:47. How long does he have to queue?

b) Lihan, Luke and Alex all want to go on the 'Thunder River' boat ride. They start queuing at 10:58 and start the boat trip at 11:26. How long do they have to queue?

c) The boat trip starts at 11:26 and lasts for 35 minutes. At what time do Lihan, Luke and Alex finish the trip?

a) Lihan and his friends have lunch at 12:15. They have to wait 6 minutes for their hotdogs to cook, queue 11 minutes at a stall for some drinks and spend 17 minutes eating and drinking. At what time do they finish eating and drinking?

b) At 13:05 the 'Wild Frontier Rodeo Show' begins! The show is made up of a 12-minute sing-a-long, 9 minutes of lasso tricks, 15 minutes of horse-riding stunts and 18 minutes of cowboys on 'bucking broncos'. At what time does the show end?

⭐Challenge

Luke and Alex's birthdays are on January 5th and March 14th. Can you work out how many days it is to their birthdays from today's date?

Measures

Measures questions can be about weight, capacity or length. Add, subtract, multiply or divide to get the answers. Remember to put in the units!

Triptonfell Rugby club has 400 litres of leek and potato soup for the spectators. One cup of soup is 250 ml. How many spectators can have a cup of soup?

Read the question then read it again

'400 litres… 250 ml…'

Choose the operation/units

How many *lots of* 250 ml in 400 litres?

Estimate

How many 250 ml in *1 litre* first of all?

Calculate

1 litre ÷ 250 ml = 4 so 400 × 4 = 1600
1600 spectators can have a cup of soup.

Check

400 divided by 0.25 = 1600

Hints and tips

★ 'Milli' means 'a thousand' in Latin. 1000 years in a millennium, 1000 mm in a metre.

★ 'Kilo' means 'a thousand' in Greek. 1000 g in a kilogram, 1000 m in a kilometre.

★ 'Centi' means 'a hundred' in Latin. 100 cm in a metre, 100 cl in a litre, 100 years in a century.

Questions

1

a) The rugby pitch is 75 m long. The groundsman lengthens it by 500 cm.
How long is the pitch now in metres?

b) One rugby ball weighs 420 g. How many kilograms does a bag of eight balls weigh?

c) Leon can kick a rugby ball 26 m. Leon's coach can kick a ball two and a half times
further. How far can the coach kick the ball?

2

a) Leon is playing in a match. He runs 45 m with the ball and kicks it a
further 12 m up the pitch. How many centimetres has the ball travelled?

b) The total weight of the forwards in Leon's team is 440 kg. The other team's forwards are
heavier by 37.5 kg. What is the total weight of both teams' forwards in kilograms?

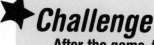 Challenge

After the game, the 30 players each drink a 330 ml can of fruit juice. The referee and two
linesmen also drink a can. How many litres of fruit juice are drunk at the end of the match?

Puzzles

Number puzzles are great fun but you have to think step-by-step to get them right! It can really help to underline key words in these questions.

Who am I? I have two digits. I am greater than 60.
I can be divided exactly by 5 and by 7.

Read the question then read it again	'I need to work methodically…'
Choose the operation/units	Dividing 2-digit numbers by 5 and 7.
Estimate	As it can be divided by 7 it must be… 63, 70, 77, 84, 91 or 98.
Calculate	The only number out of those that can be divided by 5 is 70. I am the number 70.
Check	70 ÷ 5 = 14 and 70 ÷ 7 = 10.

Hints and tips

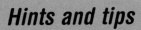 When solving puzzles, it helps to work 'methodically'.
This means taking things step-by-step.

Questions

a) Who am I? I have two digits. I am an even number. One of my digits is 3. The sum of my digits is 11.

b) Leigh Anne is thinking of a 3-digit number. It is less than 200, can be divided exactly by 10 and the sum of all three digits is 7. What number is Leigh Anne thinking of?

c) Which two numbers have a 1-digit answer when multiplied and a 2-digit answer when added?

a) The ages of Michael and Richard add up to 55. Michael's age is Richard's age reversed. How old are Michael and Richard?

b) Can you find three numbers that have the same answer when multiplied together as when added together?

★ Challenge

There are 100 buildings along a street. Sid the sign maker is ordered to number the buildings from 1 to 100. How many '9s' will he need?

Patterns and sequences

Pattern questions might ask you to find the 'nth' number in a pattern or to work out how many numbers are in the pattern. These questions are all about sport.

Here is a list of World Cup winning teams since 1966.

Year	1966	1970	?	1978	?	1986	1990	1994	?	2002
Winner	England	Brazil	West Germany	Argentina	Italy	Argentina	Germany	Brazil	France	Brazil

In which year did **a)** West Germany win the World Cup?
b) Italy win?   **c)** France win?

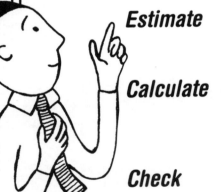

Read the question then read it again	I don't like football! Never mind, it's the numbers that matter. Three parts to the question…
Choose the operation/units	I'm looking for the difference between the years.
Estimate	1970 something, 1980 something and 1990 something.
Calculate	The difference between the years is 4. West Germany won in 1974, Italy in 1982 and France in 1998.
Check	Yes, those years fit the sequence of a World Cup being held every four years.

Hints and tips

★ When asked to predict the next number in a sequence, start looking at the rest of the numbers and how they relate to each other. Work out their differences.

Questions

a) The next World Cup will be held in 2006. When will the next three after that be held?

b) The first Rugby World Cup was in 1987. It is held every 4 years. Including the first, how many Rugby World Cups will there have been by the end of 2007?

c) Has there ever been a Football World Cup and a Rugby World Cup in the same year? Explain your answer.

a) The Football World Cup was first held in 1930. Two World Cups were cancelled because of World War Two. How many Football World Cups had there been by the end of 2002?

b) The modern Olympics were first held in Athens in 1896. They are also held every four years. Three Olympics have been cancelled because of war. How many games, including Athens in 1896, had there been by the end of 2002?

 Challenge

Football is said to have been invented during Tudor times. If Henry VIII had started the World Cup in 1542 and it was held every four years, how many World Cups would there have been by the end of 2002? Include all the World Cups that have taken place. (Assume there were no *additional* breaks for war.) What about every six years since 1542? Every nine years?

Multiplication

Multiplication problems are story problems. They are often about measures or money. The key is to work out what numbers you are multiplying and include the units!

Samoya has 7 gooseberry bushes in her garden. She picks 68 from each one to make a kilogram of gooseberry jam. How many gooseberries has she picked?

Read the question then read it again	'7 bushes... 68 from each...'
Choose the operation/units	7 *lots of* 68... multiplication.
Estimate	Round 68 to 70... $7 \times 70 = 490$
Calculate	$\begin{array}{r} 6\ 8 \\ \times\quad 7 \\ \hline 4\ 7\ 6 \end{array}$ Samoya picked 476 gooseberries.
Check	476 is close to my estimate. Also, $476 \div 7 = 68$.

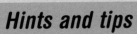

Hints and tips

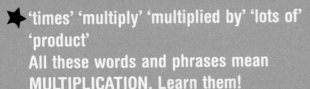

★ 'times' 'multiply' 'multiplied by' 'lots of' 'product'
All these words and phrases mean MULTIPLICATION. Learn them!

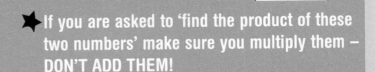

★ If you are asked to 'find the product of these two numbers' make sure you multiply them – DON'T ADD THEM!

Questions

a) Samoya and eight of her friends have a picnic in the garden. They each eat 75 g of Gooseberry jam. How many grams of jam do they eat?

b) Samoya pours 3 of her friends 320 ml of homemade lemonade. How many millilitres of lemonade has she poured?

c) Her other 5 friends prefer elderflower cordial! They have 180 ml each. How many millilitres of elderflower cordial does Samoya pour in total?

a) Two of Samoya's friends, Sasha and Sabrina, pick some strawberries. Sasha picks 14 boxes of 32 strawberries and Sabrina picks 17 boxes of 26 strawberries. Who has picked the most? By how many?

b) Sabrina makes a daisy chain with 35 daisies. It measures 60 cm. The other eight friends are impressed and they each make a daisy chain with 35 daisies measuring 60 cm. How many daisies were used, and how long would a chain be in metres, if they joined them altogether?

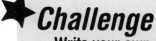

Challenge

Write your own multiplication word problem. Use your name in the problem and give it to a friend to answer!

Division

These division problems are all about a school.
Work out which number to divide (the bigger
one usually). Don't forget to put in the units!
Watch out! There are some big numbers here!

Brights Park Primary school has 288 pupils in the juniors. There are 12 equal sized classes. How many children are in each class?

Read the question
then read it again

'288... 12... how many children?'

Choose the operation/units

12 into 288. That's division.

Estimate

10 into 300 = 30

Calculate

$$\begin{array}{r} 2\ 4 \\ 1\ 2\overline{)2\ 8\ 8} \\ \underline{2\ 4} \\ 4\ 8 \end{array}$$

There are 24 children in each class.

Check

My estimate was a bit out. I'll check using the inverse method. $24 \times 12 = 288$. I was correct!

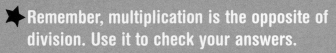

Hints and tips

★ Remember, multiplication is the opposite of division. Use it to check your answers.

★ 'share' 'group' 'divide' 'divided by' 'divided into'
All these words and phrases mean DIVISION. Learn them!

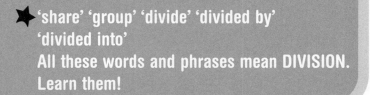

Questions

Brights Park
Infants School

1 a) Brights Park infants has 232 pupils with 8 equal classes.
How many infants are in each class?

b) Brights Park serves excellent lunches! Cook makes chocolate cakes which feed 6. How many cakes would Cook have to bake if every one of the 288 juniors had a slice?

c) Cook makes bigger chocolate cakes for the infants! Each cake feeds 4 hungry infants. If all 232 infants had a slice, how many cakes would Cook have to make?

2 a) Brights Park has been given a donation of 432 books from the local library. The books could be handed out to the 12 junior classes or the 8 infant classes. Who would receive more books per class – the infants or the juniors? How many more?

b) The Story Bus arrives at school! It can only hold 20 pupils at a time for ten-minute slots. There are 520 infants and juniors. How long does it take for all the children to visit the Story Bus?

★ Challenge

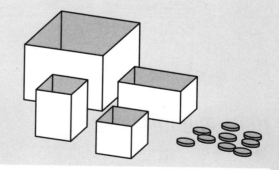

Use nine counters and four boxes.

Can you share the nine counters so that each box contains an odd number of counters? There must be a different number of counters in each box.
You must use all nine counters! Impossible? It can be done...

2D shapes

These questions all ask you to add shapes together and work out what the new shape is. If it helps, you can draw each of the questions step-by-step.

Mustapha has drawn a shape. All four of its angles are right angles, the opposite sides are equal and parallel and the diagonals bisect each other. It has two lines of symmetry. What shape has Mustapha drawn?

Read the question then read it again

Read slowly and carefully...

Choose the operation/units

I'm looking for a shape...

Estimate

A quadrilateral of some sort...

Calculate

These are the properties of a rectangle. Mustapha has drawn a rectangle.

Check

I can draw the shape myself to check.

Hints and tips

★ Use a ruler when drawing shapes.
★ Learn the language: angles, sides, equal, parallel, bisect, congruent, right angle.

Questions

1

a) Mustapha draws another shape. This one has 3 sides, which are all the same size, and all the internal angles are 60 degrees. What shape has Mustapha drawn?

b) Ali draws a shape. His shape also has 3 sides but only two of its sides are the same length. It is shaped like an arrow. What shape has Ali drawn?

c) Cem draws a star with 5 points. Each of the 5 points is the same distance apart. He then joins the points together with straight lines. What shape has Cem drawn?

2

a) A triangle has three sides. Look up the prefix 'tri' in the dictionary. List as many nouns (objects) with the prefix 'tri' as you can, e.g. 'tricycle'.

b) A quadrilateral has 4 sides. Look up the prefix 'quad' in the dictionary. Make a list of as many words as you can with the prefix 'quad', e.g. 'quadruplet'.

Challenge

Set yourself a time limit to find 14 shape related words.
Any you don't understand, look up in a dictionary.
Under 3 minutes – you're in shape!

These are the words:

heptagon	quadrilateral
polygon	hexagon
square	scalene
rectangle	triangle
parallel	octagon
isosceles	equilateral
pentagon	circle

x	h	e	p	t	a	g	o	n	l	a	w	e
p	f	b	a	d	p	e	n	t	a	g	o	n
y	g	h	p	a	z	q	v	t	g	l	o	n
i	k	s	d	r	b	u	j	s	z	m	c	e
s	e	c	j	k	c	i	r	c	l	e	t	q
q	u	a	d	r	i	l	a	t	e	r	a	l
u	i	l	e	a	q	a	t	r	a	d	g	p
a	v	e	t	u	o	t	q	i	m	b	o	o
r	u	n	g	r	h	e	x	a	g	o	n	l
e	q	e	g	d	z	r	u	n	o	h	l	y
s	o	r	e	c	t	a	n	g	l	e	c	g
t	p	a	r	a	l	l	e	l	e	f	s	o
b	m	u	i	s	o	s	c	e	l	e	s	n

3D shapes

3D shape questions will often ask you to recognise a range of 3D shapes and count them. This activity is a tricky one, so work step-by-step.

This is the Space Port of 'R-Star City' which has just experienced a terrible earthquake!

Have a close look at how it was built and see if you can answer the questions on page 37.

Hints and tips

★ 3D shapes have 'faces' (the flat parts), 'edges' (the long sharp parts) and 'vertices' (the short sharp parts where the edges meet).

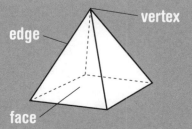

Questions

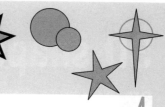

1

a) How many cylinders can you find in the power station?

b) How many prisms can you find in the passenger terminal?

c) How many hemispheres can you see in the spaceship hangers?

2

a) How many cubes are needed to repair the control tower so that it is restored to a cuboid shape?

b) How many cubes are needed to repair the 'Venus View' hotel so that it is restored to a cuboid shape?

Challenge

Complete this table to show the total number of each shape in R-Star City Space Port.

Shape	cubes	cuboids	square-based pyramids	spheres	hemi-spheres	cylinders	cones	prisms	tetrahedrons	polyhedrons	octahedrons
Number											

Position and direction

Position and direction questions will often ask you to look at a map with grid references. You will need to find the coordinates of different landmarks.

Marie is exploring the streets of Manhattan, New York. She starts from her hotel at point (1, 5) and walks 4 points east, and then turns 90 degrees clockwise. She then walks 3 points south. Which landmark is Marie standing next to? What is her new position?

Read the question then read it again

I need to work step-by-step.

Choose the operation/units

I'm working with coordinates... Remember, along then up.

Estimate

Marie is going east then south... ...United Nations or Empire State?

Calculate

Mark (1, 5) with a cross. Count 4 points east.
Turn 90 degrees clockwise. Marie is now facing south. Count 3 points south.
Marie is standing next to the Empire State building.
Her new position is (5, 2).

Check

Double-check that I'm correct.

Hints and tips

★ Coordinates mark where the lines cross, not the spaces in between.

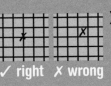

✓ right ✗ wrong

★ Remember, 'x' comes before 'y' in the alphabet. Always go ALONG the corridor then UP the stairs.

Questions

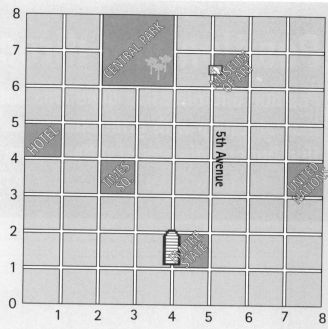

Use the map to answer
all these questions.

a) What runs from (5, 8) to (5, 0)?

b) If Marie starts at (3, 0) and walks north for 3 points,
which landmark will she be standing next to?

c) If Marie was standing at the point (3, 7), where would she be?

a) Here are three of a landmark's coordinates: (5, 6), (5, 7) and (6, 7). What is the missing
coordinate and what is the name of the landmark?

b) What are the four coordinates marking the four vertices of Central Park?

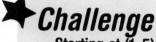 *Challenge*

Starting at (1, 5), can you describe a route visiting all six landmarks and returning to the
hotel at (1, 5)?

Data handling

Data handling questions will ask you to look at a chart, graph or table and use the data to answer the questions. Sometimes you will have to transfer data from a table to a chart.

Estelle played her favourite computer game 'Grand Theft Motors 3'.

Using the bar chart below, what was the most common way that Estelle lost a game of 'Grand Theft Motors 3'? How many times did it happen?

How Estelle lost at 'Grand Theft Motors 3'

Read the question then read it again

I need to understand what the chart is telling me...

Choose the operation/units

The chart is telling me how often a way of losing a game happened.

Estimate

I have to look at all the information that is given to me.

Calculate

The column showing the highest frequency is 'ran out of health points', which happened 6 times.

Check

I can compare my answer with all the other possibilities – yes, I'm correct.

Hints and tips

★ Look at the titles of the graph and the axes first. They tell you what the information is trying to show.

Questions

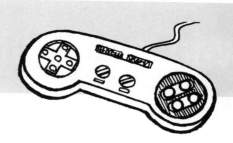

a) How many times did Estelle 'drive into the river'?

b) How many times did Estelle 'get hopelessly lost'?

c) How many games in total did Estelle lose by 'crashing and burning' and 'getting hopelessly lost'?

2 How many games of 'Grand Theft Motors 3' did Estelle play altogether?

★ Challenge

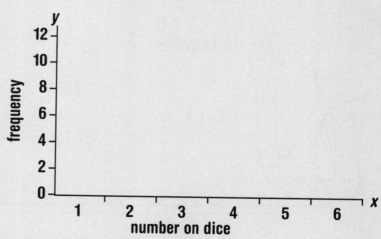

1	
2	
3	
4	
5	
6	

Roll a dice 50 times. Tally the results in the chart. Use your results to complete a frequency bar chart on the axes.

Make up three word problems based on the chart for a friend to answer.

Two-step problems

Two-step problems need you to think carefully and keep notes of each step. You will have to complete an operation, take the answer and do a further one or two operations to that answer to get the final answer.

Brights Park Primary are holding their Summer Fête. There are 50 stalls, 34 are selling things and half of the remainder are sideshow games. How many stalls are sideshow games?

Read the question then read it again	' 50… 34… half of the remainder…'
Choose the operation/units	Subtract 34 from 50 then divide the answer by 2.
Estimate	(in my head) 50 – 30 = 20 then half of 20 = 10… ten seems reasonable.
Calculate	50 – 34 = 16 then half of 16 = 8. 8 stalls are sideshow games.
Check	These are short calculations. I can redo them quickly to check.

Hints and tips

★ Work out which part of a multi-step problem needs to be done first. Always show your working when writing down how you tackled a problem.

Questions

1

a) Jackie and John are running the bric-a-brac stall. Jackie sells £18 worth of bric-a-brac and John sells £24 worth. They give £35 to the school and keep the rest for themselves. How much money do Jackie and John keep?

b) Sara and Daniel buy 3 strips of raffle tickets each. The raffle tickets cost 75p a strip. How much do they spend on raffle tickets altogether?

c) Harry and Matthew try to guess how many sweets there are in a jar. Harry says 290 and Matthew says 235. There are 255 sweets in the jar! Who was closest to the correct amount and by how many?

2

a) Livvie and Callum are running the 'throw wet sponges at the teacher' stall. They charge 30p for one sponge or 50p for three sponges. Mr Clark, the Head, is taking his turn to be soaked! Doug has £4.80 and wants to spend all of his money on throwing sponges. What is the most number of sponges Doug can afford to throw?

b) David and Stephen are running the 'pin the tail on the donkey' stall. By the end of the fête they have made £77 for the school and £15 for themselves. However, before they go home, David suggests they donate 10% of their total takings to his favourite charity. Stephen agrees. How much do they give to the charity?

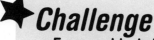

Challenge

Ewan and Isobel are running a dartboard stall.

What is the highest total you can make with three darts if each dart has to land in a separate section? What is the lowest total?

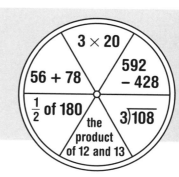

Answers

Place value

a) Three hundred and forty-six
b) Nine hundred and eighty-four
c) Three hundred and forty-eight

a) Seven hundred and fifty-two
b) One hundred

Challenge
396,471
1,019,013
49,073,001

Fractions

a) $\frac{1}{4}$
b) $\frac{1}{8}$
c) $\frac{1}{12}$

a) 35
b) 100 metres

Challenge
Yes, he does get a sloppy kiss! Wesley is 9, his granny is 81. Nine is one ninth of 81.

Decimals

a) 10.90 m
b) 15.7 seconds
c) 0.91 m

a) 24.9 seconds
b) 14 minutes

Challenge
213.7 kg

Percentages

a) £21
b) £10
c) £25

a) The one in the department store, which is £10 cheaper
b) £48

Challenge
Debbie – £50 Lee – £10 Faye – £15

Addition

a) 309
b) 234
c) 315

a) Lewis needs 108 and Derelle needs 330
b) Anna needs 289 stickers

Challenge
256 on the ninth square and 32,768 on the sixteenth square

Subtraction

a) 169
b) 83
c) 97

a) £6.80
b) 99

Challenge
From 2003, the answers are 34, 100, 166, 398, 518 and 937.

Money

a) £125
b) 7 weeks
c) £135

a) She can only buy 2 DVDs and she gets to keep £6.02
b) £35

Challenge
£1 a day for a year is the greater amount. The difference in totals is £98.36

Time

a) 42 minutes
b) 28 minutes
c) 12:01

a) 12:49
b) 13:59

Challenge
Answers will vary.

Measures

a) 80 m
b) 3.36 kg
c) 65 m

a) 5700 cm
b) 917.5 kg

Challenge
10.89 litres of fruit juice

Puzzles

a) 38
b) 160
c) 1 and 9

a) 41 and 14 or 23 and 32
b) 1, 2 and 3 (1 + 2 + 3 = 6 and 1 x 2 x 3 = 6)

Challenge
He needs 20 '9s'. One each for the numbers 9, 19, 29, 39, 49, 59, 69, 79, 89, 90, 91, 92, 93, 94, 95, 96, 97, 98 and two for 99.

Patterns and sequences

a) 2010 2014 and 2018
b) 6
c) No. The sequences will always remain at four years for both the rugby and the football World Cups. They would have to have started in the same year.

a) 17
b) 24

Challenge
115
Every 6 years since 1542? 76
Every 9 years? 51

Multiplication

a) 675 g
b) 960 ml
c) 900 ml

a) Sasha has picked 6 strawberries more.
b) The chain would have 315 daisies and measure 5.40 metres.

Challenge
Answers will vary.

Division

a) 29
b) 48
c) 58

a) The infants would receive 18 more books.
b) 26 visits of 10 minutes each = 4 hours 20 minutes

Challenge
Place one counter in one box, three in another box and five in a third one. Then place the three boxes inside the fourth box!

2D shapes

a) An equilateral triangle
b) An isosceles triangle
c) A pentagon

a) Answers will vary.
b) Answers will vary.

Challenge

x	h	e	p	t	a	g	o	n	l	a	w	e
p	f	b	a	d	p	e	n	t	a	g	o	n
y	g	h	p	a	z	q	v	t	g	l	o	n
i	k	s	d	r	b	u	j	s	z	m	c	e
s	e	c	j	k	c	i	r	c	l	e	t	q
q	u	a	d	r	i	l	a	t	e	r	a	l
u	i	l	e	a	q	a	t	r	a	d	g	p
a	v	e	t	u	o	t	q	i	m	b	o	o
r	u	n	g	r	h	e	x	a	g	o	n	l
e	q	e	g	d	z	r	u	n	o	h	l	y
s	o	r	e	c	t	a	n	g	l	e	c	g
t	p	a	r	a	l	l	e	l	e	f	s	o
b	m	u	i	s	o	s	c	e	l	e	s	n

3D shapes

a) 4
b) 2
c) 2

a) 7
b) 14

Challenge

Shape	cubes	cuboids	square-based pyramids	spheres	hemi-spheres	cylinders	cones	prisms	tetrahedrons	polyhedrons	octahedrons
Number	27	1	3	1	2	4	2	2	2	7	2

Position and direction

a) Fifth Avenue
b) Times Square
c) Central Park

a) (6, 6) Museum of Art
b) (2, 5), (2, 8), (4, 5) and (4, 8)

Challenge
Possible route: Walk north for 1 point. Turn 90 degrees clockwise. Walk east for 6 points. Turn 90 degrees clockwise. Walk south for 4 points. Turn 90 degrees clockwise. Walk west for 4 points. Turn 90 degrees clockwise. Walk north for 2 points. Turn 90 degrees anti-clockwise. Walk 2 points west.

Data handling

a) 5
b) 2
c) 6

20

Challenge
Answers will vary.

Two-step problems

a) £7
b) £4.50
c) Matthew was closest by 15

a) 28 sponges
b) £9.20

Challenge
The highest total is 454. $56 + 78$, $592 - 428$, the product of 12 and 13
The lowest total is 186. 3×20, $\frac{1}{2}$ of 180, $3\overline{)108}$

Your notes